# Baba Yaga

—— A RUSSIAN FOLKTALE ——

*retold by*
Margaret Yatsevitch Phinney

*Illustrated by*
Lydian Green

*For three special people:*

*My father, Michael, who was my consultant,*
*My son, Alexi, who offered suggestions,*
*And my sister, Stephanie, who loves me a lot.*

FIRST PUBLISHED IN THE UNITED STATES OF AMERICA IN 1995 BY
**MONDO Publishing**
Originally published in Australia in 1988 by
Horwitz Publications Pty Ltd

Text copyright © 1988 by Margaret Yatsevitch Phinney
Illustrations copyright © 1988 by Horwitz Publications Pty Ltd

For information contact:
MONDO Publishing
One Plaza Road
Greenvale, New York 11548

PRINTED IN THE UNITED STATES OF AMERICA
First Mondo printing, April 1995
95 96 97 98 99 00     9 8 7 6 5 4 3 2 1

Original development by Robert Andersen & Associates and Snowball Educational
Jacket and cover redesign by Nancy Williams

**Library of Congress Catalog Card Number: 95-5430**

# Pronouncing Glossary

**Baba Yaga** (BA-buh yuh-GA)
An old woman or witch found in many Russian folktales.

**brume** (BROOM)
From the French *la brume*, meaning "mist" or "fog."

**Izbushka** (izz-BUSH-kuh)
Baba Yaga's house that stands on chicken legs and revolves 'round and 'round when she's away.

**Kosshchei Bez Smertnyi** (koss-SHCHAY bez SMERT-nyee)
A phantom skeleton that sometimes helps Baba Yaga with her evil deeds.

**samovar** (SAM-o-var)
A large, urn-shaped metal pot with a spigot. It sometimes has an oil or a candle heater built into the base for heating water for tea.

**stupa** (STOO-pah)
A mortar of wood or bronze for grinding or pounding seeds, nuts, grains, or other foods.

Katrina lived nearby a wood
In a hut of logs and bark.
Her father was most kind and good,
But worked from dawn to dark.

At night he told her stories,
They were tales of creatures strange
That lived within the forest thick
And about its borders ranged.

The worst of all these creatures,
The one to avoid with care,
Was Baba Yaga, the fearsome witch,
For children she will snare.

"Don't go too far," he warned his girl,
"You know the reason why.
Don't go too deep into that wood.
The witch is biding nigh."

"Baba Yaga is a witch,
  In the forests of Russia she dwells.
  She walks and she stalks,
  She wanders and roams,
  While casting her evil spells."

Her father had a housemaid,
Her job to cook the meat,
To wash the pots and dishes;
Set the samovar to heat.

The housemaid hated 'Trina,
Who was so good and kind,
And plotting to get rid of her,
Was always on her mind.

She teased and pinched poor 'Trina
When her father was away.
She made her work at jobs too hard
Every moment of the day.

While 'Trina struggled with her tasks
And the housemaid raved and ranted,
Her father's deep-voiced admonitions
Inside her head she chanted:

"Baba Yaga is a witch,
   In the depth of the forest she dwells.
   She cackles and crackles,
   She screeches and laughs,
   When children are caught
      in her spells."

One day an impulse stirred the maid;
She had the perfect plan!
She'd send Katrina to the place
So feared by child and man.

"Take this basket to your aunt,
She lives within the wood.
Follow the straight and narrow path,
Stay on it as you should.

"There's a slab of salted bacon,
A loaf of good, fresh bread,
A wheel of cheese, and a jug of milk,
For your aunt, who's sick in bed."

Katrina did not know, of course,
That the witch lived on that track.
The housemaid sent her off, you see,
In the hope she'd not come back.

Baba Yaga is a hag,
Her face is so bitter and stony.
She clacks and she cracks
With teeth cast of iron.
Her hands are all gnarled and bony.

Katrina skipped along the path,
Her heart was full of gladness.
A visit to her dear old aunt
Would surely lift her sadness.

Birdsong filled the morning air,
The path was straight and bright,
Butterflies and cheerful flowers
Were everywhere in sight.

But slowly, slowly as she walked
The trees closed in the way;
The path began to twist and turn
And gloom shut out the day.

The songs of birds were seldom heard
And flowers then were rare;
She sensed a growing gloominess
And closeness in the air.

Baba Yaga is a witch,
In a stupa of bronze she does fly.
She guides as she rides
With a pestle of oak,
And a broom sweeps her tracks
from the sky.

Around a bend, along the track,
Stretched out beside a log,
She saw upon the path, near death,
A parched and panting dog.

"Katrina, please, a sip to drink,
My burning throat is dry.
Another hour in this state,
And I will surely die."

Katrina took the jug of milk
From the basket on her arm.
She gave the dog a long cool drink
And kept him thus from harm.

"Oh thank you!" said the happy dog.
"Now I've advice for you.
When you must flee this gloomy wood,
Come here — I'll help you through."

Baba Yaga is a witch,
She stirs up the wind as she goes.
It howls and it yowls,
It whistles and moans;
The trees are bent low as it blows.

She came around another curve
And there within her view,
She saw a rusted wrought iron gate,
Neglected and askew.

"Please, Katrina, take that rag
And grease my hinges 'round.
I cannot bear another day
This screeching, grating sound."

From the grate she plucked the rag
And bacon fat she took.
She rubbed the hinges in and out
In every smallest nook.

"Thank you," sighed the grateful gate.
"Now you should keep the rag,
It has a bit of magic yet,
'Twill save you from the hag."

Baba Yaga is a witch,
In Izbushka, the hut, is her home.
It walks and it stalks,
It revolves 'round and 'round.
On the legs of a chicken it roams.

Shrouded in a thick grey mist,
—The girl could hardly see—
A portal to a clearing
The gate turned out to be.

As 'Trina started through the field,
Her pace began to slow;
Her body felt like leaden weight,
And fear within did grow.

Then suddenly before her
A hut loomed from the brume;
Its scaly feet tramped 'round and 'round;
It bore the smell of doom.

Katrina slumped into a heap,
Frightened and dismayed.
'Twas then she knew the horrid truth:
By the maid she'd been betrayed.

Baba Yaga is a witch,
Izbushka is at her command.
She yells out a spell
As she storms into view,
And low bends the hut on demand.

Katrina felt a lashing wind
Whip 'round her in a blast.
She saw the witch come roaring in,
But the numbness held her fast.

"Ha ha!" screeched out the ugly hag
  When she saw where 'Trina lay.
"A sweet and tender little girl
  To eat some future day."

  She stood Katrina on her feet
  And spoke an incantation.
"'Til then I'll get some work from you;
  Izbushka needs attention."

  Izbushka ceased its tramping
  And the door was opened wide.
Baba Yaga shoved 'Trina in
And locked her tight inside.

Baba Yaga is a witch,
She searches for tubers and plants.
With potions and lotions
She brews her concoctions,
Strange liquids and spells
    she decants.

The witch went off in search of herbs
And left the girl to sweep.
Izbushka held her fast inside.
Katrina could only weep.

The witch returned by evening
And ate a huge repast.
'Trina had but a crust of bread
To break her day-long fast.

Too tired and sad to eat her food,
She curled up in a heap.
She wished her father could be near
As she sobbed herself to sleep.

That night a scrawny cat lay down
And curled within her arm.
She gently stroked its matted fur;
It didn't take alarm.

Baba Yaga is a crone,
She's lived her long life all alone.
She's lean and she's mean,
She's selfish and cold,
Her age is too great to be known.

"Please comb me out, dear 'Trina,"
  Softly mewed the cat.
"The snags and knots, they pull and pain,
  But the witch cares nought of that.

"There's a comb upon the mantle,
  Use that to pluck each burr."
  Quietly 'Trina fetched the comb
  And smoothed the straggled fur.

"Keep the comb my gentle friend,"
  The cat purred softly near.
"'Twill help you flee the awful witch
  Just when her grasp you fear.

"When midnight strikes its deepening hour,
  That's when you make your flight.
  The witch falls in her deepest sleep
  At that hour of the night."

Baba Yaga has a helper,
Kosshchei Bez Smertnyi is he.
He screaks and he creaks,
He rattles and moans,
A thin bony phantom to see.

At the midnight hour Katrina rose
And crept across the floor.
With trembling hand she raised the latch,
And slipped out through the door.

She groped her way across the field
'Til she reached the forest's frame,
Then followed it 'round until she found
The path on which she came.

She reached the gate, which opened wide
And let her pass on through,
Then swiftly, quietly, locked itself;
The witch would get her due.

Though Baba Yaga slept deeply,
Kosshchei Bez Smertnyi did not.
He saw Katrina run away
And longed to see her caught.

Kosshchei Bez Smertnyi's a scoundrel,
Though his power is only to scare.
He prattles and tattles;
He's deceptive and sly.
The witch gets his help with
    her snares.

To Izbushka flew this phantom rack
And gave the witch a shake.
"She's out! She runs! You'd best be off!"
At once the witch was awake.

The hag rose up in anger
And cursed the cat full sore.
"Why did you not spit fire at her
And stop her at the door?"

"She cared for me as you have not,
She helped me in my need,
She put my pain before her own;
I repaid her kindly deed."

In rage the witch kicked at the cat
Which fled across the floor.
As Baba Yaga took up the chase
Her spite grew more and more.

Baba Yaga is a shrew,
She's abusive to those she'd
    command.
And cruel is her rule,
She's spiteful and harsh;
She controls with a heavy hand.

In a leap she reached the forest's edge,
But the gate blocked passage through.
She gave the command to open up,
Her bidding it would not do.

"What's this?" the witch, impassioned, cried.
"My gate defies me, too!
  Why did you not cut off her path
  When she was passing through?"

"She cared for me as you have not,
  She eased my galling pain.
  She earned the help she got from me;
  To her you'll lay no claim."

  The witch her teeth in fury gnashed,
  Then climbed the stubborn gate
  And vanished down the twisting path
  To seal Katrina's fate.

Baba Yaga is a scold,
She rages whenever she's mad.
She mutters and sputters,
She frets and she foams,
She's moody, quick-tempered,
   and bad.

Katrina was nearly breathless;
The witch was gaining fast.
Her gasping lungs were burning;
She knew she could not last.

Suddenly she remembered:
The comb she quickly found,
And turning back the way she came,
She tossed it on the ground.

A wall of trees sprang from the earth,
Twisted, tangled, tall.
They were so thick and densely grown,
That none could pass at all.

The witch shrieked out her madness.
She tore her hair in rage;
In fury shook the tree trunks
Like a wild cat in a cage.

Baba Yaga is sharp-sighted,
She can see in the dimmest of shades.
She leers when she peers,
She's so sure of her prey,
Her vision is keen as a blade.

Katrina did not stop to rest,
But slowed a bit her pace.
Then suddenly the path was gone,
Was lost without a trace!

The dog appeared before her,
There to save the day.
"The witch did this to trick you;
By those oaks you'll find the way."

And then she heard the witch again,
A howling, growling sound.
The hag had taken up the hunt:
She'd found a way around.

By the trees Katrina found the path,
And down the track she flew.
She was gone before the wicked witch
Came within her view.

Baba Yaga is a witch,
But her sorcery does have a bound.
If her prey should stray . . .
If it leaves the wood,
The witch will be forced
    to turn 'round.

Katrina heard the witch's roar
When she found her trap had failed.
And all around the wind did rage
As she ranted and she railed.

"You didn't stop her," screamed the witch,
"You withered, wailing, wretch!"
"You didn't feed me," yelped the dog.
"That girl you'll never catch!"

The witch howled out her anger
And tore off upon the path.
She lashed the trees and bit the leaves,
While stumbling in her wrath.

Katrina struggled frantically
To reach the forest bound,
For the witch's power leaves her there,
And she'd be safe and sound.

Baba Yaga is a devil,
She doesn't give up 'til she's won.
She sneaks and she peeks,
She tries every chink,
She cackles in triumph when done.

The crashing grew more noisy
And the wind began to pound.
'Trina could feel the heavy breath
As the wicked witch gained ground.

"The rag! The rag!" her mind called out.
"Use the magic rag!"
  She pulled it from her apron sash
  And tossed it at the hag.

  And instantly a lake appeared;
  It blocked the witch's path.
  She thundered up and down its edge,
  Beside herself in wrath.

"I'll have you yet!" she bellowed,
"For none escape my hold."
  And she waded in the frothy lake
  So grey, and deep, and cold.

Baba Yaga is a fury,
She simply can't bear not to win.
Danger's a stranger,
And she loses her wits,
When she thinks she will have
    to give in.

She wallowed through the water,
And when she could not wade,
She took the plunge to swim across;
Rage made her unafraid.

Her robes became all sodden,
They dragged her down and down.
The last Katrina saw of her
Was the witch's angry frown.

Katrina reached her cottage.
Her father met her there.
His worried face broke in a smile;
He'd been searching everywhere.

He sent the housemaid packing
And dismissed their cares with laughter.
They did the chores together
And lived happily thereafter.

Baba Yaga was a witch,
The forest had long been her claim.
She walked and she stalked,
She wandered and roamed.
Now all that remains is her name.